Jonah
and the Whale

Andrew McDonough

This is the great city of Nineveh.
From a distance it looks like a nice place to visit.

But when you reach the front door,
it doesn't seem quite so friendly.

When you get inside and meet the locals,
you might wish you'd never come.

Here is the king of Nineveh with his 'How far can I throw
visitors over the wall?' machine. His record is 352 cubits.

Here are some ancient carvings from Nineveh.

If you are on holidays, it is best not to visit Nineveh.

One day God sent a message to Jonah.

Jonah liked the idea of God being angry with the people of Nineveh but he did not like the idea of warning them. They might start behaving and not get in trouble. Besides, he didn't want to help the king break his 'throwing visitors over the wall' record.

So Jonah hopped on a boat to Tarshish and sailed off into the sunset away from Nineveh, away from God.

God sent a huge storm with big black clouds and boat-breaking waves.

"Help!" cried the captain.

"Save us!" prayed the sailors.

"Snore, snore, snore," went Jonah.

"Wake up, Jonah!" yelled the captain, "and pray to your god."

"Whose fault is this?" asked the sailors as they began drawing straws. "Mine," said Jonah, holding the short straw. "I'm running away from God, and I think he just caught up with me. You'd better toss me in the sea."

But God sent a whale to swallow Jonah.

For three days and three nights Jonah was inside the whale. It was too dark to read; besides, he didn't have a book. He couldn't watch television because he didn't have a television. So Jonah prayed, "Thanks, God, for saving me. I will do what you asked."

Then the whale swam up to the beach and "Blaaark," out popped Jonah.

God sent a message to Jonah a second time.

Jonah knocked on the front door of Nineveh. It opened, and in he marched.

When the king heard Jonah, he realised that, while he enjoyed throwing visitors over the wall, it was not fun for the visitors. So the king stopped being nasty, put on his "I'm sorry" clothes and asked God to forgive him. Everyone in Nineveh did the same.

Here are some more ancient carvings.

Jonah was . . .

furious!
There wasn't going to be an "or else!"
He stormed out of Nineveh.

Jonah sat outside the city and fumed.

God grew a bush to
shade Jonah.

Jonah was happy
about the bush.

The next day God sent a worm to munch on the bush.

Jonah was angry at the worm. He was also angry at Nineveh and angry at God. Then God sent another message to Jonah.

Dear Jonah,
Hot enough for you?
You care about the bush
that gave you shade.
I care about the people,
the girls and boys, and
the animals in Nineveh.

Shouldn't you?

Lots of love God

Cecil's Page

Hi Friends,

Jonah and the Whale is based on the Old Testament book of Jonah. You can use this story to teach children about the compassion of God for his people. (By the way, have you noticed that the Bible has lots of stories that include one of the best parts of God's creation . . . animals?)

Before the story

You can begin by saying:

"This is a BIG story with some BIG things in it! See if you can spot the BIG things in the story. And at the end we'll see if you spotted the BIGGEST thing of all."

Read the story

After the story

Ask, "What big things did you spot in the story?"
"What was the biggest thing of all?"
(Here are my top BIG things: The big BADDIES in the city of Nineveh. The big JOB Jonah was given. The big RUNNER Jonah did when God called him. The big STORM. The big U-TURN. The big REVIVAL when the Ninevites turned to God. The big DUMMY SPIT.)

Your child will probably say the Whale is the biggest thing they spotted? A good answer, but even he's just a tiddler compared to the GREAT BIG LOVE OF GOD in this story!

God's Blessings,

Cecil

Jonah 1:1–3 (CEV)

One day the LORD told Jonah, the son of Amittai, to go to the great city of Nineveh and say to the people, "The LORD has seen your terrible sins. You are doomed!" Instead, Jonah ran from the LORD. He went to the seaport of Joppa and bought a ticket on a ship that was going to Spain. Then he got on the ship and sailed away to escape.

First printing July 2006
15 14 13 12   10 9 8 7 6 5 4 3

National Library of Australia
Cataloguing-in-Publication entry

Author:	McDonough, Andrew (Andrew John)
Title:	Jonah and the whale / Andrew McDonough.
Publisher:	Unley, S. Aust. : Lost Sheep Resources, 2008.
ISBN:	9781921229190 (pbk.)
Series:	McDonough, Andrew (Andrew John). Lost sheep. Series 2 ;7
Subjects:	Jonah (Biblical prophet)--Juvenile literature.
	Bible stories, English--Juvenile literature.
	Picture books for children.
Dewey Number:	224.92

Ship's captain: Stewart Bogle
First mate: Luke Bogle
This book is water resistant to a depth of 30 metres.

Designed and published by Lost Sheep
Distributed by Authentic Media in partnership with Lost Sheep
Printed in Singapore by Tien Wah Press Pte Ltd
Authentic Media, 52 Presley Way, CrownHill, Milton Keynes, MK8 0ES, United Kingdom
Lost Sheep, PO Box 3191, Unley SA 5061, Australia
info@lostsheep.com.au
lostsheep.com.au